From Found to Crown

A HEALING JOURNAL FOR WOMEN OF FAITH

EMMA JAE BROWN

Welcome to your Journey Ladies!

It takes a strong woman to want to heal...to want to grow deeper in her relationship with Christ. Although you have accepted Him as your Lord and Savior and are intentional about your prayer life and time in the Word, do you sometimes feel as though there is a disconnect?

It is a road I know all too well. For a long time, I felt like there was something wrong with me...as though I was somehow lacking. My internal thoughts just didn't seem to align with being a daughter of the kingdom. Then, I found a way to heal and embrace my identity as daughter of the Most High. So if you feel as though you too are in need of transformation, let's get started!

"Take my yoke upon you and learn from me, for I am gentle and humble in heart, and you will find rest for your souls."

MATTHEW 11:29

How are you...*Really?*

The first time somebody asked me this question with absolute interest, I could instantaneously feel my face begin to flush. As tears threatened to flow, I had to take a deep breath and break away momentarily from the conversation.

How could I be so unaware that I was NOT okay?

How could I be so disconnected from myself?!

Reacting to such a simple question in such an emotional way forced me to step back and seriously feel my way through my soul. Once I took the time to sit down with myself, it came to me: it was ALL performative. Everything I was doing was performative. Nothing simply flowed

from my soul...nothing was flowing from love. I was simply doing what I thought I was supposed to be doing.

No wonder I was so exhausted!

That's the day I decided to stop. I decided to follow the directions I had been given, and simply rest until I was able to find a way to change my approach. I decided that if what I was doing didn't flow from a natural place within me, then it was a lie.

I knew that God did not want me living a lie. Nor did he want me living as an exhausted, emotional shell of a person.

Now, my story is not necessarily your story. However, if you feel as though you are in need of spiritual healing, this is the first crucial step. Don't be afraid to dig deep...God wants this for you.

How am I feeling today...*Really?*

"My dear brothers and sisters, take note of this: Everyone should be quick to listen, slow to speak and slow to become angry."

JAMES 1:19

Learning to Listen

I don't know about you, but I adore analogies. As an author, it gives me so much more space to work with. So in that spirit, I want you to sit back, close your eyes, and envision your feelings as roadmaps.

This goes beyond simply knowing what you think about something. Do your best to articulate what you are feeling in your body at this exact moment. Are you comfortable? Or perhaps are you slightly cold or slightly warm? Hungry? Tired from a long day? All of the feelings present in your body lead you to make a choice in order to meet your physical needs.

⟵⟶

My friend, God gave us our emotions for exactly the same reason! While many prefer to refer to it as intuition rather than "feelings" or "emotions", they are a gift! He wants us to be able to use what we are feeling to guide us...so that we can make the choices that will fulfill our spiritual needs.

It takes practice to learn to decipher the path your emotions are leading you on, but with time it will become second nature. In a quiet environment, sit back and really listen to how you feel about your situation. Do you need to pray about it? Do you need to forgive or seek forgiveness? Do you need to let go of control and trust in Him?

What are my feelings telling me? What do I need from myself?

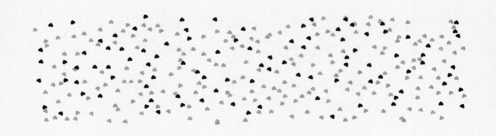

"And now these three remain: faith, hope and love. But the greatest of these is love."

CORINTHIANS 13:13

Responding to Yourself with Compassion

Being fully known by our Lord means that we are bestowed with priceless favor. Along with unlimited and boundless love, we are offered gifts such as truth and grace.

As we travel further on our walk with our Savior, we learn how to embrace and embody these ideals of love, truth, and grace as we attempt to live out the Great Commission (Matthew 28:16-20).

We know it is critical to love the Lord our God with all of our hearts, minds, and souls. Likewise, we grasp the importance of delving this same love to our neighbors in hopes that they will meet Jesus on their journeys as well.

How often do you extend this same love, truth, and grace to yourself?

This has been an immense struggle in my life. It took me years to recognize that I too, am worthy of the grace that I so freely extend to others.

Perhaps you are here as well. The difficulty resides in our *knowing*. We are able to recall with precision all of our own sins. We keep detailed records of our owns thoughts and deeds which are SO not Christ-like.

We become ruled by the shadows of our former selves.

Trust me when I say I know exactly how this feels. But my friend, that's what the cross is for...to relieve us of these burdens so that we can live freely. So how about trying it today?

Just for today, walk alongside your former self; the woman you used to be who may have lied or cheated.

Wrap your arm around the wounded little girl that was you...that was too jealous or self-serving.

Give her some compassion. Tell her that you understand her; that you know why she did what she did, whether it was due to ignorance or the need to survive. Then let her know that she can let it all go now.

Remind her that since you've made the decision to follow Jesus, there is no more condemnation. That means freedom for every part of you...forgiveness for Every. Part. Of. You.

Then, wake up and do it again tomorrow. Because every day that you ask God to heal your heart is another chance for him to say "yes".

⟵⟶

What is it that I need to give myself compassion for today?

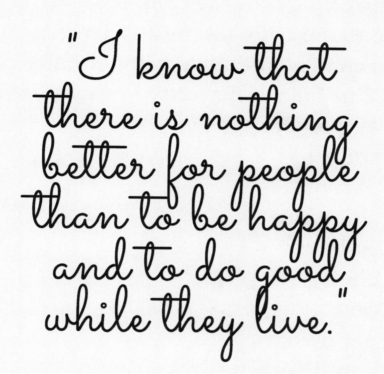

"I know that there is nothing better for people than to be happy and to do good while they live."

ECCLESIASTES 3:12

Self Care for the Real World

As a woman, by now you realize that there are multiple different types of "tired". Of course I would never be able to describe the multiple roles that each woman plays in her daily life, but for the majority of us we are:

- employees
- spouses
- parents
- children
- siblings
- chefs
- housekeepers
- pet owners
- bookkeepers
- volunteers
- friends

... and although I could continue with the list, the duties of being a woman seem to be endless.

That is EXACTLY why our joy should be endless as well! Ladies, we MUST give up the narrative that our self-care can be summed up in a spa day montage! While these days of pampering have their place within the umbrella of overall health and beauty maintenance, our personal well being consists of SO MUCH MORE!!

We need to start thinking of self-care as every nutritious thing that we feed every part of ourselves each day. This is (of course) the actual food we consume, but also the books we read; the music we listen to; the time we spend in nature or with our family, friends, or pets. It is the rest we get and relationships we build and the seeds that we are sowing each day that will reap the good fruit that we are promised!

$\longleftrightarrow$

Here are some self care ideas that you can utilize in under ten minutes each day:

Journal Your Feelings

Get Fresh Air

Drink Water

Pray or Meditate

Choose Whole Foods

⟵⟶

...and of COURSE you should still indulge in a great massage or manicure from time to time! The critical point here is that if self-care isn't contributing to the well-being of your ENTIRE temple, then a new strategy might be neccessary!

Although it will take time to turn these practices into habit, the peace that will come from knowing that you are honoring what you have been given by God is well worth the process!

←——————————→

How did I respond to and care for the needs of my temple today?

"For I know the plans I have for you," declares the Lord, "plans to prosper you and not to harm you, plans to give you hope and a future."

JEREMIAH 29:11

Setting Healthy Boundaries

    While setting healthy boundaries is a form of self-care, it is such a critical component that it deserves its own category. Since God's plans are to PROSPER us...NOT to harm us...and to give us hope for a future, it is important that we take necessary steps to ensure that the world does not harm us, either.

    This is where the relationship you have with yourself; your understanding of your own wants and needs becomes cornerstone. Now that you have worked through some of the previous steps and are connecting with the Lord and the best possible version of You, you have an idea about your identity. This identity should shape your boundaries...what you will and will not tolerate.

Your boundaries do not ever have to be loud or unreasonable...they simply need to be rooted in truth and grace. After all, it is in truth and grace that the true essence of biblical love is founded.

There will be many times in our lives and under a variety of circumstances where our boundaries are challenged; so many in fact that it would be impossible to capture the essence here in totality. Since we KNOW, however, that people of this world will intentionally attempt to cross our lines, it is imperative that we build those solid lines long before anybody arrives.

The boundaries that you build will consist of a multitude of your values and where they derived from. The key here is knowing what you unequivocally believe and value.

Think of it as though you refused to put your vehicle in "drive" until all passengers have their seatbelts on. Of course you are concerned about their safety (love), but you are also concerned about the law (truth). While it is impossible to control the actions of the other people, you have already decided your course of action long before the situation arises.

The thing about setting healthy boundaries is that you don't have to necessarily explain yourself. You simply have to be able to voice, "that doesn't work for me."

So I encourage all of you lovely ladies to consider what it means for you to love others and live under the truth in all aspects. Decide what your lines are according to what God wants for you. Then, reject any behaviors or circumstances that don't align.

Today I enforced healthy boundaries by:

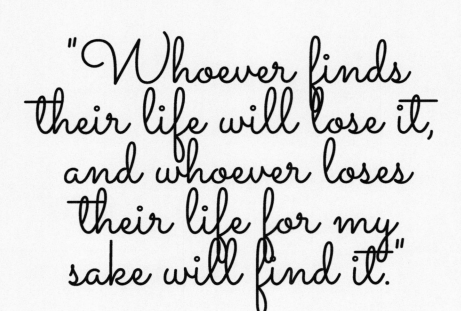

"Whoever finds their life will lose it, and whoever loses their life for my sake will find it."

MATTHEW 10:39

Living Beyond Yourself

By this point in the journey, my prayer is that you are beginning to develop a beautiful relationship with yourself in the way that our Heavenly Father intended. Becoming intimate with yourself and intimate with Him is glorious in and of itself, but it was never God's intention for us to stop here.

As we get better at caring for ourselves, we will inevitably receive the call to care for others. It is by design that we should turn back and offer to others the grace and truth (love) that has transformed us. When we show that to others, they are able to catch a glimpse of Jesus!

There are multiple ways to live beyond yourself, and the good news is that as long as you are doing it selflessly, you really can't go wrong!

While there are multiple opportunities to serve others both in your church and your community, it can be a daunting choice if you have never volunteered before. The advice below will help you to explore your options so that you can be great while walking out the Great Commission.

1 *Pray about it.*
GOD ALREADY GAVE YOU THE HEART FOR YOUR CAUSE.

2 *Use Your Strengths*
NOT EVERYBODY HAS THE SAME ONES!

3 *Find the Need*
SOMEBODY NEEDS EXACTLY WHAT YOU ARE OFFERRING!

⟷

Even though it may be too ambitious to attempt to volunteer every day, we can bring our compassion for others into every situation that we face.

We all have neighbors, local schools, retirement homes, and libraries nearby. In the majority of even moderately sized cities there are food banks and pet shelters. Our Lord and Savior Jesus Christ came to serve, not to be served. To grow deeper with ourselves and him, we can find ways to positively impact our communities.

As we develop deeper relationships with Christ we will become more like Him in seeking out ways to help those in need and positively impact our communities.

Today I brightened somebody's day by:

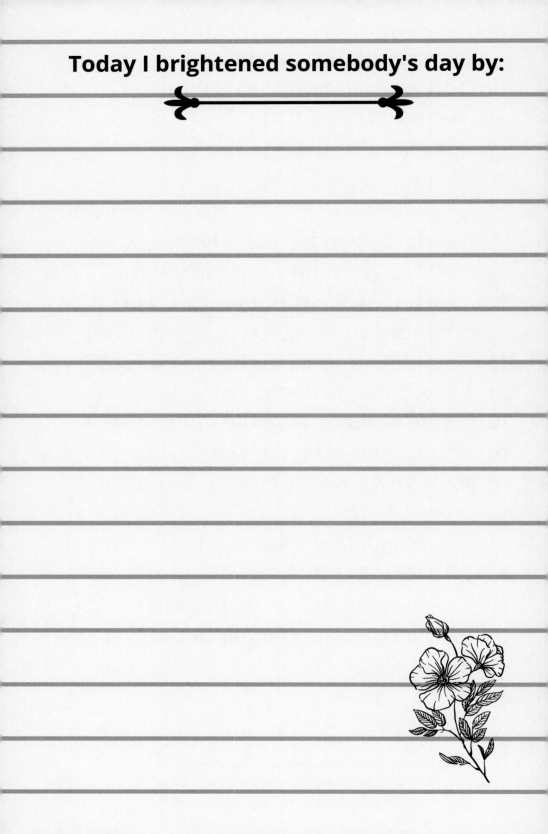

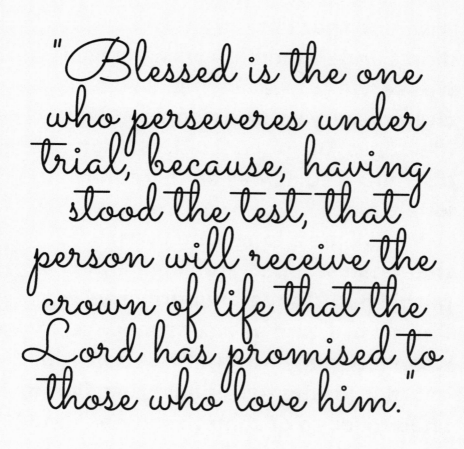

"Blessed is the one who perseveres under trial, because, having stood the test, that person will receive the crown of life that the Lord has promised to those who love him."

JAMES 1:12

Growing in Grace

Perhaps it was inevitable for me, but there came a point in my walk with God that I hit a spiritual wall. I didn't understand it. I was giving...I was serving...I was loving...I was in church every week listening to the messages. Despite all of this, I felt disconnected. It was an incredibly lonely place.

It took me a long time to realize that I had stopped growing in my faith. I had stopped hungrily seeking God's word, and as a consequence, I wasn't leaning into that relationship. In order for me to rekindle that flame, I had to let go of something that I am certain plagues many of you ladies...

PERFECTIONISM.

For me, this seemed to be the most daunting and insurmountable task.

But, I had to let go.

I had to let go of the vision of myself that I was holding on to so tightly. I had to openly admit that I was just as broken on this day as I was on the first day...Even though, I'd come so far in my journey. I had to realize my utter dependence on my Savior, and then and ONLY then was I able to dive deeper into the relationship.

God wants us to grow...for our ENTIRE lives. The process is never complete, until we have persevered and been given our Holy Crowns by the Most High.

So are you ready?
The real journey still awaits.

⟵⟶

How am I growing intentionally closer to God and his grace today?

"A wise
man will
hear and
increase
learning."

PROVERBS 1:5

My Hope for You

   I am so honored that I could be a part of the beginning of your journey. I want to invite you to continue for the next month. If you are able to commit to this, I am certain that it will create small habits within you that will allow you to grow continuously into the crown you were born to wear.

Your friend in Christ,

   Emma Jae

How am I feeling today...*Really?*

_____

_____

_____

What are my feelings telling me?
What do I need from myself?

_____

_____

_____

What is it that I need to give myself compassion for today?

_____

_____

_____

How did I respond to and care for the needs of my temple today?

_____

_____

Today I enforced healthy boundaries by:

_____

_____

Today I brightened someone's day by:

_____

_____

How am I growing intentionally closer to God and his grace today?

_____

_____

How am I feeling today...*Really?*

_____

_____

_____

What are my feelings telling me?
What do I need from myself?

_____

_____

_____

What is it that I need to give myself
compassion for today?

_____

_____

_____

How did I respond to and care for the needs of my temple today?

_____

_____

Today I enforced healthy boundaries by:

_____

_____

Today I brightened someone's day by:

_____

_____

How am I growing intentionally closer to God and his grace today?

_____

_____

How am I feeling today...*Really?*

_____

_____

_____

What are my feelings telling me?
What do I need from myself?

_____

_____

_____

What is it that I need to give myself compassion for today?

_____

_____

_____

How did I respond to and care for the needs of my temple today?

_____

_____

Today I enforced healthy boundaries by:

_____

_____

Today I brightened someone's day by:

_____

_____

How am I growing intentionally closer to God and his grace today?

_____

_____

How am I feeling today...*Really?*

_____

_____

_____

What are my feelings telling me?
What do I need from myself?

_____

_____

_____

What is it that I need to give myself compassion for today?

_____

_____

_____

How did I respond to and care for the needs of my temple today?

_____

_____

Today I enforced healthy boundaries by:

_____

_____

Today I brightened someone's day by:

_____

_____

How am I growing intentionally closer to God and his grace today?

_____

_____

How am I feeling today...*Really?*

_____

_____

_____

What are my feelings telling me?
What do I need from myself?

_____

_____

_____

What is it that I need to give myself compassion for today?

_____

_____

_____

How did I respond to and care for the needs of my temple today?

_____

_____

Today I enforced healthy boundaries by:

_____

_____

Today I brightened someone's day by:

_____

_____

How am I growing intentionally closer to God and his grace today?

_____

_____

How am I feeling today...*Really?*

_____

_____

_____

What are my feelings telling me?
What do I need from myself?

_____

_____

_____

What is it that I need to give myself compassion for today?

_____

_____

_____

How did I respond to and care for the needs of my temple today?

_____

_____

Today I enforced healthy boundaries by:

_____

_____

Today I brightened someone's day by:

_____

_____

How am I growing intentionally closer to God and his grace today?

_____

_____

How am I feeling today...*Really?*

_____

_____

_____

What are my feelings telling me?
What do I need from myself?

_____

_____

_____

What is it that I need to give myself compassion for today?

_____

_____

_____

How did I respond to and care for the needs of my temple today?

_____

_____

Today I enforced healthy boundaries by:

_____

_____

Today I brightened someone's day by:

_____

_____

How am I growing intentionally closer to God and his grace today?

_____

_____

How am I feeling today...*Really?*

_____

_____

_____

What are my feelings telling me?
What do I need from myself?

_____

_____

_____

What is it that I need to give myself compassion for today?

_____

_____

_____

How did I respond to and care for the needs of my temple today?

_____

_____

Today I enforced healthy boundaries by:

_____

_____

Today I brightened someone's day by:

_____

_____

How am I growing intentionally closer to God and his grace today?

_____

_____

How am I feeling today...*Really?*

_____

_____

_____

What are my feelings telling me?
What do I need from myself?

_____

_____

_____

What is it that I need to give myself compassion for today?

_____

_____

_____

How did I respond to and care for the needs of my temple today?

_____

_____

Today I enforced healthy boundaries by:

_____

_____

Today I brightened someone's day by:

_____

_____

How am I growing intentionally closer to God and his grace today?

_____

_____

How am I feeling today...*Really?*

_____

_____

_____

What are my feelings telling me?
What do I need from myself?

_____

_____

_____

What is it that I need to give myself compassion for today?

_____

_____

_____

How did I respond to and care for the needs of my temple today?

_____

_____

Today I enforced healthy boundaries by:

_____

_____

Today I brightened someone's day by:

_____

_____

How am I growing intentionally closer to God and his grace today?

_____

_____

How am I feeling today...*Really?*

_____

_____

_____

What are my feelings telling me?
What do I need from myself?

_____

_____

_____

What is it that I need to give myself compassion for today?

_____

_____

_____

How did I respond to and care for the needs of my temple today?

_____

_____

Today I enforced healthy boundaries by:

_____

_____

Today I brightened someone's day by:

_____

_____

How am I growing intentionally closer to God and his grace today?

_____

_____

How am I feeling today...*Really?*

_____

_____

_____

What are my feelings telling me?
What do I need from myself?

_____

_____

_____

What is it that I need to give myself
compassion for today?

_____

_____

_____

How did I respond to and care for the needs of my temple today?

_____

_____

Today I enforced healthy boundaries by:

_____

_____

Today I brightened someone's day by:

_____

_____

How am I growing intentionally closer to God and his grace today?

_____

_____

How am I feeling today...*Really?*

_____

_____

_____

What are my feelings telling me?
What do I need from myself?

_____

_____

_____

What is it that I need to give myself compassion for today?

_____

_____

_____

How did I respond to and care for the needs of my temple today?

_____

_____

Today I enforced healthy boundaries by:

_____

_____

Today I brightened someone's day by:

_____

_____

How am I growing intentionally closer to God and his grace today?

_____

_____

How am I feeling today...*Really?*

_____

_____

_____

What are my feelings telling me?
What do I need from myself?

_____

_____

_____

What is it that I need to give myself compassion for today?

_____

_____

_____

How did I respond to and care for the needs of my temple today?

_____

_____

Today I enforced healthy boundaries by:

_____

_____

Today I brightened someone's day by:

_____

_____

How am I growing intentionally closer to God and his grace today?

_____

_____

How am I feeling today...*Really?*

_____

_____

_____

What are my feelings telling me?
What do I need from myself?

_____

_____

_____

What is it that I need to give myself
compassion for today?

_____

_____

_____

How did I respond to and care for the needs of my temple today?

_____

_____

Today I enforced healthy boundaries by:

_____

_____

Today I brightened someone's day by:

_____

_____

How am I growing intentionally closer to God and his grace today?

_____

_____

How am I feeling today...*Really?*

_____

_____

_____

What are my feelings telling me?
What do I need from myself?

_____

_____

_____

What is it that I need to give myself
compassion for today?

_____

_____

_____

How did I respond to and care for the needs of my temple today?

_____

_____

Today I enforced healthy boundaries by:

_____

_____

Today I brightened someone's day by:

_____

_____

How am I growing intentionally closer to God and his grace today?

_____

_____

How am I feeling today...*Really?*

_____

_____

_____

What are my feelings telling me?
What do I need from myself?

_____

_____

_____

What is it that I need to give myself compassion for today?

_____

_____

_____

How did I respond to and care for the needs of my temple today?

_____

_____

Today I enforced healthy boundaries by:

_____

_____

Today I brightened someone's day by:

_____

_____

How am I growing intentionally closer to God and his grace today?

_____

_____

How am I feeling today...*Really?*

_____

_____

_____

What are my feelings telling me? What do I need from myself?

_____

_____

_____

What is it that I need to give myself compassion for today?

_____

_____

_____

How did I respond to and care for the needs of my temple today?

_____

_____

Today I enforced healthy boundaries by:

_____

_____

Today I brightened someone's day by:

_____

_____

How am I growing intentionally closer to God and his grace today?

_____

_____

How am I feeling today...*Really?*

_____

_____

_____

What are my feelings telling me? What do I need from myself?

_____

_____

_____

What is it that I need to give myself compassion for today?

_____

_____

_____

How did I respond to and care for the needs of my temple today?

_____

_____

Today I enforced healthy boundaries by:

_____

_____

Today I brightened someone's day by:

_____

_____

How am I growing intentionally closer to God and his grace today?

_____

_____

How am I feeling today...*Really?*

_____

_____

_____

What are my feelings telling me?
What do I need from myself?

_____

_____

_____

What is it that I need to give myself compassion for today?

_____

_____

_____

How did I respond to and care for the needs of my temple today?

_____

_____

Today I enforced healthy boundaries by:

_____

_____

Today I brightened someone's day by:

_____

_____

How am I growing intentionally closer to God and his grace today?

_____

_____

How am I feeling today...*Really?*

_____

_____

_____

What are my feelings telling me?
What do I need from myself?

_____

_____

_____

What is it that I need to give myself
compassion for today?

_____

_____

_____

How did I respond to and care for the needs of my temple today?

_____

_____

Today I enforced healthy boundaries by:

_____

_____

Today I brightened someone's day by:

_____

_____

How am I growing intentionally closer to God and his grace today?

_____

_____

How am I feeling today...*Really?*

_____

_____

_____

What are my feelings telling me?
What do I need from myself?

_____

_____

_____

What is it that I need to give myself compassion for today?

_____

_____

_____

How did I respond to and care for the needs of my temple today?

_____

_____

Today I enforced healthy boundaries by:

_____

_____

Today I brightened someone's day by:

_____

_____

How am I growing intentionally closer to God and his grace today?

_____

_____

How am I feeling today...*Really?*

_____

_____

_____

What are my feelings telling me? What do I need from myself?

_____

_____

_____

What is it that I need to give myself compassion for today?

_____

_____

_____

How did I respond to and care for the needs of my temple today?

_____

_____

Today I enforced healthy boundaries by:

_____

_____

Today I brightened someone's day by:

_____

_____

How am I growing intentionally closer to God and his grace today?

_____

_____

How am I feeling today...*Really?*

_____

_____

_____

What are my feelings telling me?
What do I need from myself?

_____

_____

_____

What is it that I need to give myself compassion for today?

_____

_____

_____

How did I respond to and care for the needs of my temple today?

_____

_____

Today I enforced healthy boundaries by:

_____

_____

Today I brightened someone's day by:

_____

_____

How am I growing intentionally closer to God and his grace today?

_____

_____

How am I feeling today...*Really?*

_____

_____

_____

What are my feelings telling me?
What do I need from myself?

_____

_____

_____

What is it that I need to give myself
compassion for today?

_____

_____

_____

How did I respond to and care for the needs of my temple today?

_____

_____

Today I enforced healthy boundaries by:

_____

_____

Today I brightened someone's day by:

_____

_____

How am I growing intentionally closer to God and his grace today?

_____

_____

How am I feeling today...*Really?*

_____

_____

_____

What are my feelings telling me?
What do I need from myself?

_____

_____

_____

What is it that I need to give myself compassion for today?

_____

_____

_____

How did I respond to and care for the needs of my temple today?

_____

_____

Today I enforced healthy boundaries by:

_____

_____

Today I brightened someone's day by:

_____

_____

How am I growing intentionally closer to God and his grace today?

_____

_____

How am I feeling today...*Really?*

_____

_____

_____

What are my feelings telling me?
What do I need from myself?

_____

_____

_____

What is it that I need to give myself compassion for today?

_____

_____

_____

How did I respond to and care for the needs of my temple today?

_____

_____

Today I enforced healthy boundaries by:

_____

_____

Today I brightened someone's day by:

_____

_____

How am I growing intentionally closer to God and his grace today?

_____

_____

How am I feeling today...*Really?*

_____

_____

_____

What are my feelings telling me?
What do I need from myself?

_____

_____

_____

What is it that I need to give myself compassion for today?

_____

_____

_____

How did I respond to and care for the needs of my temple today?

_____

_____

Today I enforced healthy boundaries by:

_____

_____

Today I brightened someone's day by:

_____

_____

How am I growing intentionally closer to God and his grace today?

_____

_____

COMING SOON!

The next step in your journey to becoming a "Whole Woman"...

Made in the USA
Coppell, TX
10 April 2021